the total runner's log

the essential training tool for the runner

Dr. Sharon L. Svensson

The Trimarket Company • Palo Alto • California • USA

the total runner's log

the essential training tool for the runner

by Dr. Sharon L. Svensson

Published by: The Trimarket Company
2264 Bowdoin Street
Palo Alto, California 94306, USA

Cover photography: Tony Svensson (endurance athlete Paul Huddle at Emigrant Pass in the 1997 Western States Endurance Run)

Production: This book was created using FrameMaker® from Adobe Systems, Inc. on PowerBook® and Power Macintosh® computers from Apple Computer, Inc. Pace chart calculations were completed using AppleWorks™ from Apple Computer, Inc. The artwork was produced using Illustrator® and the photos edited using Photoshop® from Adobe Systems, Inc.

Printed at Patson's Media Group, California, USA

ISBN: 1-887565-04-3
Third edition

Personal Information

If found, please return. This log contains information that is considered vital to its owner.

Name	
Address	
How to reach me	phone: fax: email: mobile phone:
Best time and place to reach me	
Affiliation(s)	
In emergency, call	
Sports physician	
Medical details	
Log period	start: end:

Contents

Introduction

The Total Runner's Log is designed for runners. It enables you to keep a daily record of your running and related activities. The log also provides information about nutrition, heart rate monitor training and strength training.

The best way to improve your running is to keep track of your progress. A well-organized written record will keep you honest. Just as a checkbook allows you to keep track of your finances, this log will help you monitor the state of your physical health and well-being. *The Total Runner's Log* has two main components:

1. A distillation of running secrets. The advice is short and to the point.

2. A support structure of log pages, to help you keep track of where you've been, where you are and where you're going. The log pages are undated.

By keeping a record, you'll stay motivated and on track. But remember: you train to get fitter and faster, not to have the world's best-looking log. The log can best help you monitor your progress if you keep your system simple.

THE LOG PAGE STRUCTURE

There are four types of log pages: the weekly overview, the specialized logs, the summary logs and the race record. The weekly overview pages can be used to keep track of your daily workouts. The other pages allow you to keep more in-depth records. For example, the specialized interval and strength training pages provide more space to detail your favorite workouts; the summary logs will help in your long-term evaluation. The log section contains:

• Weekly overviews (53 pages)

• Specialized logs
   - Interval training (4 pages)
   - Strength training (4 pages)

• Annual summary (2 pages)

• Racing
   - Pace charts (4 pages)
   - Race record (1 page)

• **Weekly overview.** There are 53 weekly overviews, each with five blank columns in which to record your aerobic (running) and nonaerobic (strength training, stretching, etc.) activities. Some people prefer to use several of the columns for body weight, morning heart rates, hours and quality of sleep, workout intensity and so on. The design of the page is intentionally open-ended; you can personalize it for your own desired level of detail. For ideas on how to use the overview, you can look at the sample weekly overview on page 82.

- **Interval training.** One of the keys to getting faster is to incorporate interval sessions into your program. For the average runner, intervals can be short, predetermined periods at a slightly higher pace or intensity. For the more performance-oriented runner, intervals are carefully mapped-out sessions with periods of intense effort and calculated rests. There are four interval pages.

- **Strength training.** This is where you record your specific strength workouts, in detail. You may have one or more upper body programs, lower body programs and abdominal programs, depending on the season and other factors. Each program gets its own page so you can better track your progress and any workout modifications. Since it is unlikely that you will have more than a few different strength programs, there are four of these pages.

- **Annual summary.** In the back are two summary pages, the annual summary table and the annual graph. As your weekly overviews start accumulating, you simply transfer the weekly totals and/or averages to the table and then to the graph. Filling out and analyzing the summary pages can help you better understand your progress. Specifically, you may find correlations between, on the one hand, your running load, weight, morning heart rate, calorie consumption, hours of sleep and work/travel schedule, and on the other, your performance or feeling of well being.

- **Racing.** There are four pace charts (two metric and two using the US system of measurement) on pages 94 to 97, should you be more competitively inclined. There is also a race record form on page 100.

BEFORE YOU BEGIN TO TRAIN

As well as being a complete record keeping system, *The Total Runner's Log* also contains a distillation of concrete exercise and nutritional advice. (This book, however, is not an exhaustive manual on training, exercise physiology or nutrition.) Regardless of the shape you're in, before you begin a new running season, it is advisable to heed this warning from the American College of Sports Medicine:

At or above 35 years of age, it is necessary for individuals to have a medical examination and a maximal exercise test before beginning a vigorous exercise program. At any age, the information gathered from an exercise test may be useful to establish an effective and safe exercise prescription. Maximal testing done for men at age 40 or above or women age 50 and older, even when no symptoms or risk factors are present, should be performed with physician supervision.

LIVE HEALTHIER AND RUN FASTER

Dr. Walter M. Bortz, II, a distance runner and the author of *We Live Too Short and Die Too Long,* has summarized the primary truths about health:

> When I address a group, I say to the audience, "Health is three things." Members of the group inhale and ready their pencils. Then I announce, "Good nutrition, adequate rest and ample exercise." The collective exhale is palpable as I imagine their thoughts. "Boring, boring, boring. Have I given up my day to hear this yahoo doctor tell me that health is rest, nutrition and exercise? What a waste of time!"

He then goes on to show why his statement is true, and why most people ignore it—which is beyond the scope of this log. But he is absolutely right. The principles and guidelines that follow are the things you most need to know about health and fitness. They will help you *enjoy* running while staying healthy and injury free.

1. Evaluate your present fitness level and set a realistic initial goal. Have a healthcare professional knowledgeable in sports OK your proposed program.

2. Record your efforts. Keep a training diary or daily log, such as the one included in this book.

3. Performance = Stress + Rest. To achieve your maximal performance, you need to maximize all the parts of the equation. Doing so requires sensible and innovative train-

ing, as well as very serious rest. To learn when your body needs either exercise or rest is to learn how to train. Therefore, it is critical that you listen to what your body is telling you at all times. Learn to distinguish between the muscle discomfort that results from hard exercise and the more serious pain in joints, tendons and ligaments that may later result in injury, if unheeded. To decrease the risk of injury, develop and follow a hard/easy schedule. This means, for instance, that you *never* run hard or long on two consecutive days. If you are tired, rest, don't train!

4. Establish your own long-term running schedule. The exercise cycle is stress-rest-stress. Your system reacts to the stress, recovers and gets stronger during the rest, and is then ready for more stress. Each of us can stand different loads and needs different amounts of time to adapt. *You are an experiment of one.* Establish your own running schedule; do not follow anyone else's. Listen to your body. You have to give your body time to adapt to training over a longer period of time.

5. Be heart smart. Learn how to take your pulse or heart rate (on the side of your neck just below your jawline or on your wrist). Also, consider buying a heart rate monitor. The effects of training are monitored by time, distance and intensity. Although it is possible to gauge intensity by perceived effort, there is a direct correlation between intensity and heart rate. Not only is this measure more accurate than your perceived effort, it is easier to record, compile and analyze. (See page 26 for more information on more advanced training with a heart rate monitor.)

6. Record your morning heart rate. Upon wakening and while still in bed, take your pulse. As your fitness improves, your morning resting heart rate will drop. If you have a heart rate of five to ten (or more) beats per minute (bpm) higher than your morning norm, you have not recovered from your previous day's exercising or whatever long- or short-term stress you've exposed your body to—including anxiety, lack of sleep and extended travel. You may also be catching a cold or fighting off some other illness. Take the day off.

7. Weigh yourself regularly. If you are overweight, you may not lose much weight initially—but soon you should lose up to half a kg (one pound) per week. Running consumes no more than 1,000 kilocalories per hour. (The bigger you are, the more calories you consume.) There are approximately 7,000 kilocalories per kg of fat (3,500 per pound).

8. Run on an empty stomach. Run at least three hours after your last meal. Running too soon after eating cause increased peristalsis, cramps, and, for some, even diarrhea. A bowel movement beforehand may prevent these abdominal symptoms.

9. Stay well-hydrated before, during and after exercise. A good rule of thumb is to drink as much as your stomach can handle every 20 minutes or so. Most people tolerate water best, particularly in hot temperatures. In hot and humid weather, drink more! There are many sports drinks on the market, some better than others—experiment with them in training before using them in a race.

10. Wear the right clothes. In cold weather, wear several thin layers of clothing to protect against the wind and wet. In hot weather, wear light-colored clothes, ultraviolet (UV) protective sun glasses and a visor or cap.

11. Be careful if you run on the road. Run on the side of the road with traffic coming toward you—so you can see it. At night, wear some reflective material as close to the ground as possible, so the drivers can see you. And don't wear a Walkman.

12. Use sunscreen. Wear a waterproof sunscreen if you go out in the sun, preferably one with a sun protection factor (SPF) of 15 or more. Look for a "broad spectrum" sunscreen with two or more UV absorbing ingredients.

13. "Bellybreathe." Bellybreathing requires practice, and you should do it deliberately just prior to running. Take air into your belly and exhale against a slight resistance. This helps prevent getting a "stitch."

14. Warm up and warm down. Gradually warm up at the

beginning of each run to decrease the risk of injury. Warm down at the end of each run to help speed recovery and prepare for your next run.

15. Wait for your second wind. It takes about five to ten minutes and a one-degree rise in body temperature to shunt the blood to the working muscles. When this happens, you will begin to sweat lightly and your breathing will be easier—this is your second wind.

16. Run economically. Do not bounce or overstride. You should lengthen your stride by pushing off, not reaching out. Do not let your foot get ahead of your knee. Your knee should be slightly bent at footstrike. Run from the hips down with the upper body straight up and used only for balance. Relax.

17. Stretch vigorously only after a workout. Before running, do only very light stretching, if any: start out very easily for five to ten minutes, stop to stretch if you like, and then resume your running. *The University of California, Berkeley Wellness Letter* advises: "Don't bounce when stretching, since this actually tightens muscles. The best kind of stretch is the 'static' stretch, where you gradually increase the stretch without straining the muscles. Although recent studies have failed to show that stretching after a too strenuous workout heads off muscle soreness, it does promote flexibility and can keep your muscles from tightening up quickly."

18. Learn to read your body. Be aware of overtraining signs. If the second wind brings a cold, clammy sweat, head for home. Be alert to impending trouble. Loss of zest, light-headedness, scratchy throat, swollen glands, insomnia or palpitations are signs of trouble ahead.

19. Do not train when you have a cold. A cold indicates that you have some sort of infection in your body. You might be overtrained, overstressed or both. Wait a few days before you train again—take a nap during the time you would normally have spent on the road.

20. Be alert for signs of injury. Most running injuries result from some drastic change. A change in shoes, an increase in weekly distance or intensity, hill work and so on are all factors that can increase your susceptibility to injury. In running, there is almost always some associated weakness of the foot or a strength/flexibility imbalance. Or, one leg is shorter than the other. Use of heel lifts, arch supports, orthotics, shoe modifications and corrective exercises *(particularly stretching)* may be necessary. The more you run—especially if running is your only exercise—the more muscle imbalance occurs. The calf, hamstring and lower back muscles become short, tight and inflexible. They have to be *stretched!* The shin, quadriceps and belly muscles become relatively weak. They must be *strengthened!*

21. Strength train. Strength training is essential for optimum performance (see page 23). We lose muscle mass during prolonged nonresistance exercise, such as running. We also lose more muscle mass as we get older.

22. Cross-train. Before you get injured, find a cardiovascular substitute for running. If you already do cross-train, it's simple to maintain your fitness level. If you don't, *The Total Fitness Log* or *The Total Triathlon Almanac* will help you explore alternative ways to stay fit.

23. If you get injured, back off. Go to a specialist in sports injuries (a good chiropractor, medical doctor or physical therapist). When you return to training, do not try to make up for lost time; your body won't accept it. Start up gradually!

24. When injured, RICE. For minor strains, sprains and tendonitis, **R**est your injured part, **I**ce for a maximum of 15 minutes, **C**ompress (or support) by lightly wrapping a towel around the injury and **E**levate the injured part above heart level. You can safely reapply ice every two to three hours for the first one to two days after these minor injuries. If your pain or injury is sharp, or persists for more than a few days, get professional advice.

25. Do not cheat on your sleep. Add an extra hour of sleep during heavy training periods. Take one or two naps, if possible.

26. Don't train right before you go to bed. Avoid exercising within a couple of hours of bedtime—it may "rev up" your system and make it hard to go to sleep.

27. Find compatible partners. Don't run with people who go substantially faster than you all the time. Every once in a while, such a "speed session" is good for you, but once a week is probably sufficient. A more prudent game plan to avoid injury or overtraining would be to run with a "speed group" one weekend and a "long distance group" the other, thus alternating between speed and distance.

28. Develop an annual training cycle. If you are serious about improving your running performance and plan to run for many years, or a lifetime, develop an annual plan. Endurance athletes have developed schedules (or "cycles"), mostly annual, consisting of four main parts: the "off" season, base training, precompetitive and competitive seasons. Your off season could be one or several months long. If you go through one of these cycles in a calendar year, your base training could be four to six months. Your precompetitive season, when you start to incorporate serious interval sessions, could be two to three months, and your competitive season no more than three months.

One of the primary sources of these guidelines is the running guru George A. Sheehan, M.D. (1918-1993), the author of Personal Best *and* Running to Win. *It is difficult to write about running and mention something he hasn't already addressed.*

Nutrition

You are what you eat. Contrary to popular belief, developing and maintaining a healthy diet is not difficult. In order of importance, here is what your body requires:

1. Water. Seventy percent of your body weight and 85 percent of your muscles are water. Basic to all life, it is your body's essential lubricant and plays a critical role in regulating your temperature and flushing out waste products, among other things. So training without an ample supply of water before, during and after is bad news, indeed.

2. Macronutrients: carbohydrates, fats and protein. You need a lot of these. They provide energy and are the building blocks your body uses to repair and renew itself.

3. Micronutrients: vitamins, minerals and enzymes. Though they are essential for life, you need them in much smaller amounts. Micronutrients are like spices in cooking: essential to enhance the recipe, but only in moderate quantities. Large amounts may spoil the dish.

TEN STEPS TO A BETTER DIET

The following is a list of guidelines, based partly on the actual practices of athletes (and the nutritional authorities who work with them, such as Dr. Philip Maffetone) and partly on publications from the National Academy of Sciences, the National Institute of Health and the American Heart Association.

1. Balance your diet. Eat a diet consisting largely of complex carbohydrates, but don't cut out all fats and proteins. Approximate percentages of caloric intake are listed in Table 1. Some endurance athletes maintain a diet consist-

Carbohydrates	Fats	Protein
50 to 60%	20 to 30%	20 to 30%

Table 1: A common diet for the active person

ing of 40 percent carbohydrates, 30 percent fats and 30 percent protein with great success. Dr. Maffetone, and many of the athletes he works with, are proponents of the 40-30-30 diet, but he also states: "I've never found a magic formula. You may have needs that demand a 50-25-25 diet, while other athletes will best operate on a 60-20-20 diet. The key to finding your optimal diet is just that—find it."

2. Look for complex carbohydrates first. A common "healthy diet" consists primarily of green leafy vegetables and starchy vegetables, grains, fruits, some dairy products and fish or poultry. Some endurance athletes, however, believe in eating red meat and even blood products several times a week, particularly during the heaviest phases of training and racing.

3. Limit your intake of saturated fats. Some fats are good and others are not; saturated fats contribute to high blood cholesterol levels. Most unsaturated ("good") fats are liquid at room temperature, while saturated fats are not.

4. Get your protein from low-fat sources. Seafood, poultry, lean meats and eggs are considered the best sources of animal protein. The list of non-animal protein sources is long. It includes beans, peas, nuts and seeds, though the latter two can be high in fats.

5. Avoid too much sugar. Many foods high in sugar are also high in fat, and sugar promotes tooth decay. Though virtually fat free, the many energy drinks on the market are loaded with sugars. Drink them only in conjunction with exercise; otherwise drink water. Dr. Maffetone comments, "I feel strongly about saying that it's the refined sugar in our diet that causes so many health and fitness problems. Excess insulin production is an important factor since it may inhibit endurance. I always say 'avoid sugar and sugar containing foods as much as possible.'"

6. Limit your intake of dietary cholesterol. Since your body produces most of the cholesterol it needs in your bloodstream, you should limit your daily intake to 300 mg. On the other hand, Dr. Maffetone maintains that "The body only absorbs 2 to 4 mg of cholesterol per kg of body weight. And most people can eat much more than 300 mg of cholesterol per day without elevating their blood cholesterol. Some wonderfully nutritious foods (such as eggs) are avoided because they contain supposedly too much cholesterol."

7. Make your own informed decision about vitamins. Vitamin supplementation may be the most controversial topic of all—some health authorities recommend against it—still, many athletes take extra vitamins. So, if you like, supplement your diet with vitamins and minerals. Multivitamins, calcium, iron and vitamin C seem to be the most popular. But be aware of overdosing on vitamins A and D, in particular.

8. Eat intelligently throughout the day. Eat a good, high-protein breakfast, then a light lunch. Save the carbohydrates for the meal after the workout to replenish muscle sugar. Try to replace lost calories as soon after you exercise as possible. Eat several small meals rather than one or two large ones.

9. Avoid processed foods. The fresher the food, the better. If people have tinkered with it, it's probably not as healthy as it was directly from the tree, plant or stream. If food comes in a natural wrapping, as a banana does, you can almost never go wrong. The second best is frozen food. A distant third is dried, vacuum packed or canned.

10. Hydrate well. Again, drink water as often as you can. When you feel hungry or "anxious for something" it may just be a sign of dehydration. Try a glass of water first. Then, if that doesn't do it, eat something.

The nutrition chapter was compiled and written with the help of Dr. Phil Maffetone. He is an applied kinesiologist with a Bachelor of Science degree in human biology and a Doctorate in Chiropractic. He has treated and trained many national and world-class athletes, such as runners Lorraine Moller and Priscilla Welch, triathletes Mark Allen and Mike Pigg, race car driver Mario Andretti and baseball's Tom Seaver, to name a few.

Hydration Secrets

1. Don't wait for a race to hydrate. Drink water throughout the day, especially the week before an event. Drink smaller amounts all day rather than two or three large doses.

2. Have a water bottle near you at all times, and make drinking water a habit. In particular, keep water near you during work hours (at your desk, by the phone) or wherever else you spend your time.

3. Eat some sodium rich foods (vegetables, sea salt and soy sauce) regularly, especially during hot weather and the week before an event.

4. Get used to drinking water before, during and immediately after training. Simulate race conditions by drinking water during fast-paced workouts. Learn to drink without swallowing air. Remember that following heavy sweating, complete water replacement may take 24 to 48 hours.

5. Discover which drinks with carbohydrates, sodium and other electrolytes you tolerate well and feel the best after consuming. Experiment during training rather than during a race.

6. Don't drink too much. Going to the bathroom every half hour, particularly if you're in a race, is too often.

Running Tips

The following is a list of running-specific tips that complement the general guidelines in the introduction.

EQUIPMENT

Buy only top-quality brand-name shoes. For training, you may want a heavier shoe with more cushioning; for racing, a lighter shoe (such as a racing flat). Larger people need more cushioning and support.

Go to a running store staffed by runners and tell them you want a good shoe. Ask salespeople whether they are runners and what kind of running they do.

Don't be timid. If they have firsthand experience with running, they are delighted to spend time with you and introduce you to their running gear and accessories. They will ask what kind of running you do (distance, surface, and so on) and analyze the characteristics of your gait (such as pronation or supination, heel striking or forefoot striking).

The shoes you buy should be as comfortable as bedroom slippers, yet give the support your feet need based on your gait. If they don't immediately feel exactly right, don't buy them. For long-distance running, they should be long enough to allow one thumb's width from your longest toe to the end of the shoe while you are standing. For shorter distances, this "rule of thumb" does not apply; you need slightly smaller and lighter shoes. If you want to run both, you need two, or more, pairs of shoes.

Aside from excellent shoes, the props needed for running are minimal. Wear what feels most comfortable to you, depending on the weather and your mood.

THE THREE BASIC TRAINING LEVELS

This section is divided into three levels: adapting to running, structuring your runs by length and intensity, and adding intervals. It can be used by beginners, as well as accomplished runners. There are also two overviews that outline daily and weekly run ranges for each of the three levels, starting on page 84.

I. Adaptation. You first need to get mentally and physically used to a regular exercise regimen. Your cardiovascular system, muscles, joints, tendons and mind need time to adapt. There are no shortcuts, though some people adapt more quickly than others. This phase lasts one month to one year, depending on your goals and initial fitness.

II. Structure. Next, you structure your runs into hard

the total runner's log

and easy days. You also introduce long, slow distance (LSD) runs. You may want to schedule your longer runs for the weekend and the hard runs for during the week (since they demand less time). With your harder and distance activities, you will test your body to find out your strengths and weaknesses, and discover your tendencies for injury. This phase lasts six weeks to six months—or a lifetime. If you are interested in just maintaining a healthy lifestyle, the workouts at this level are perfect. If you want to make racing part of your running activity, then move on to phase three when you are ready.

III. Intervals. You introduce speed and interval sessions only if your goals are more ambitious and you wish to further improve your running skills. This phase tests your body at a more advanced level and prepares you for racing. Keep in mind that this is a hard level to maintain; even world-class runners rotate their annual schedule between periods of running and not running intervals.

ADAPTING TO RUNNING

Running places a certain amount of stress on your body, so it's important to give your muscles and joints time to adapt. Start out slowly; don't do too much, too soon!

Important: If you've never run before, read this entire chapter carefully. If you're more experienced and you've been out of commission because of illness or injury, try former track runner and world-class triathlete Joy Leutner's foolproof base building program, starting on page 16.

Your back, hips, legs and feet have to endure a pounding of many times your body weight over long periods. Running on hard pavement or concrete only adds to this stress. In fact, concrete can be 50 times as hard as a soft trail.

Finally, you must *enjoy* the experience. It is hard to stick to a regular program that makes you miserable. Most of those who say they hate it probably push themselves too hard, beyond what's appropriate for their level of fitness.

Thirty and three. Start by jogging for 30 to 45 minutes two or three times a week. Separate your runs by at least one day of rest. Go out for a predetermined time, not distance. Jog a little, then walk a little at first, if you need to. Stay within your comfort zone. Find a pace at which you can carry on a conversation. If you push too hard, you may get injured and you won't look forward to doing it again.

Running style. Your style is as individual as your personality, so it's important to not worry about form at this point—just relax and do what comes naturally. Drop your shoulders, and swing your arms loosely with your fingers relaxed. As you run, look around, enjoy the day, and let your mind wander for a while. Then return to the task at hand and notice how your body feels.

After a while you will be jogging more and walking less. After three to six weeks, include some hills, but again, don't push too hard. Pace yourself and take the downhills easily. Listen to your body. When you are comfortable jogging along "indefinitely" you can try to run at an easy pace for 45 minutes—or an hour—without stopping.

Keeping a record. Log your workouts: how much you ran, how much you walked and how you felt. Starting out at 30 minutes three to four times a week will give you a mileage base of about 12 miles (about 20 km). Increase your mileage no more than 10 percent each week; otherwise you may injure yourself. If your partner is a more accomplished runner, make sure you do not let your partner determine your starting pace. Go easy. Be patient.

Setting goals. Look ahead to where you'd like to be in one month, six months, a year, and so on. You can use races to set goals for yourself, but don't start with a marathon. There are plenty of shorter races around; they are great fun and a wonderful way to meet interesting, healthy people with priorities like yours. Select a foot race six weeks to three months down the road, and develop a training plan for it. Both the 5 km (5 km = 5K = 3.11 miles) and the 10

km distances are good choices.

A FOOLPROOF BASE BUILDING PROGRAM
World-class triathlete Joy Leutner (formerly Hansen) uses a safe eight-week build-up program. (This program is based on one originally developed by running coach Robert Vaughn.) It is used by beginners, as well as by top athletes who have been injured and are looking for a "foolproof" way to get back on track.

Joy describes her program as follows: "The first week, I run 30 minutes the first day, then 20 minutes the next day, then 30 minutes the following day, and so on." The second week, she runs two-thirds of the distances of the first week, for recovery. Table 2 on page 17 shows the formula she uses. She runs every day.

It is essential to run with an easy, steady effort. Do not run *any harder* than the program allows: "Go slowly and work on your turnover [leg speed] more than your stride length." Joy suggests you run lightly on your feet: "It's a light prancing. I picture myself with a parachute and a harness lifting my weight up. Or, run like an Indian, quietly with your feet. Run tall and quietly."

Also, do not run *any longer* than the schedule allows: "You don't need to run long distances, but be sure to run every day—as long as your body is healthy enough to do so."

Week	Formula	Minutes	Type
1	X	30/20	Build up
2	2/3 X	20/13:30	Recover
3	X + 10%	33/22	Build up
4	X + 20%	36/24	Build up
5	2/3 (X + 20%)	24/16	Recover
6	X + 30%	39/26	Build up
7	X + 40%	42/28	Build up
8	X + 50%	45/30	Build up

Table 2: The eight-week consistency formula for the 10 km run

Though the distances in Table 2 are for the 10 km run, the same formula can be used for virtually any activity. For instance, the program is ideal for somebody who wants to embark upon a walking program. Joy uses her "minutes program" for all types of aerobic activities during her base period of training.

ADDING STRUCTURE

When you feel ready, you can add some structure to your workouts. Your goal now is to develop your leg speed, strength and endurance. This involves three types of workouts. You do each once a week. You can also add one more day of running per week: a short, easy run, to avoid two consecutive hard or long workouts.

Leg speed. The fartlek workout develops leg speed. *(Fartlek* is a Swedish word meaning *speed play* and it is just that: unstructured intervals of variable length and intensity.) After a five- to ten-minute warm-up, increase the pace—or even sprint—for a short time, and then jog again. Fartlek is unstructured: you vary your speed according to how you feel. Play with it. For instance, run harder between every other telephone pole or mailbox. The total distance for this run should be four to six miles (6 to 10 km).

Strength. The "tempo run" develops strength. This hard, steady run should cover two to four miles (3 to 6 km), at a pace you can maintain for that distance. Another strength workout is a brisk, hilly run. As you approach a hill, get up on your toes and lift your knees. Push your arms down and back, and pump yourself up the hill. Run the downhills with short, quick steps. Your hips should lean forward and your body float (or almost fall) down the hill.

Endurance. The long, slow distance (LSD) run develops endurance. Most people save this run for the weekend. It should be approximately twice as long as your average run. Remember, never do any of these three runs (leg speed, strength or endurance) on consecutive days. You need that easy day in between to recover.

YOUR RUNNING STYLE

As you increase the intensity of your workouts, start monitoring your running style. Try to become more efficient. Look ahead about 20 feet (5 to 10 m). Relax your facial muscles and jaw; drop your shoulders. Swing your arms loosely at your sides, and avoid crossing them over the body's centerline (this wastes energy). Your hands are cupped and relaxed (not clenched). All motion is forward; everything is relaxed. Visualize the form of a good runner you admire, and mimic that form. For long-distance running, a shorter, quicker, almost shuffling type of step is more efficient and less stressful. It is good form to land on the outside of the heel, roll inward and push off with the big toe. Changing your running form takes time. Be patient.

ADDING INTERVALS

With intervals, you alternate a hard and an easy pace. You run intervals to increase your leg speed and strengthen your heart muscle. This type of training also teaches you to run fast when your body is already tired and your muscles are under stress. You should perceive interval running as hard, but far from impossible.

Don't attempt interval training unless you have been running for at least six months and are comfortable on steady runs of at least an hour, *and* unless you run three or four times a week. When you first introduce intervals, decrease your weekly mileage by about 10 percent so your body can adapt to the new stress. To begin with, do only one interval workout per week, in place of the fartlek run. Later on, you can restore the fartlek run to your program.

Interval running has four variables: number of repeats, distance, run time and recovery time. These are listed in the interval training log (starting on page 86).

Determining your recovery time. There are three basic ways to determine the length of your recovery interval. First, you can take your pulse manually. Second, you can use a heart rate monitor (see page 26). And third, you can monitor how you feel. You don't want too little rest, because you want to finish each run evenly and in control, but you obviously don't want too much rest either.

How to run intervals. If possible, use a track, or measure out one quarter to one mile on a flat road (or, in the metric system, measure out 500 to 1,500 m). On the track, run one-milers (four laps) or 1,500 m at the same pace (or faster than) you'd run a 10 km race. During these sessions, warm up by running slowly for about 15 minutes; then run three to four one-milers, walking up to one lap of the track for recovery between each mile. Then run slowly for 15 to 30 minutes to warm down. If possible, run intervals with friends; they are excellent motivators and can monitor your running form.

To prepare for shorter races, run 400 m intervals at about 1:40 to start with. After a few weeks, try eight 400s at 1:40 with 2:00 rest. Then you can start to cut your running times, but it's best to maintain the two-minute rest period at this point in your training. Using nonmetric measurements, you would run 440 yards a few seconds slower, but maintain the two-minute rest period.

Intervals should not wipe you out. They are only a preliminary test, not the final exam. You should leave the track feeling pleased to have challenged yourself and confident that you could do more if you had to. After only a few interval sessions, you will run more comfortably and efficiently at a quicker pace and be able to run faster while fatigued. This, in turn, will do wonders for your confidence, and confidence is essential to racing well.

Advanced intervals. If you are competitively inclined and an experienced runner, it is likely that you are already dividing your life—and running—into a season and an off season. (The season would then probably consist of the base-building, precompetitive and competitive phases.) The following chart may give you some ideas about the different types of intervals you can pursue. Each will give

Type/Set	Reps	Distance	Time	Rest
Pyramid for a 40 min 10 km performance	8	400 m	1:30	1 min
	4	1,000 m	3:50	2 min
	2	2,000 m	8:00	3 min
Pyramid for a 34 min 10 km performance	8	400 m	1:13	1 min
	4	1,000 m	3:20	1.5 min
	2	2,000 m	6:40	2.5 min
Base building	6-8	1,000 m		2 min
Precompetitive	6-8	1,000 m		1.5 min
Competitive	6-8	1,000 m		1 min
Test intervals	4	2,000 m		1 min

Table 3: Sample intervals for the 10 km run

you a thorough "run for your money." You may want to get a heart rate monitor (see page 26) to better gauge your effort and recovery times.

The recoveries (rest) must be under your aerobic threshold. The test interval workout, however, is a special case. Here you run at your target race pace and simply monitor your recovery heart rate. Ideally, during the last recovery it will be the same as during the first.

If it is, you are fit and should be able to run your target time for the 10 km race—barring weather, hills and other circumstances that make life exciting. The chapter "Running Your Best Race" on page 21 outlines how you actually can accomplish such a feat.

Beyond *The Total Runner's Log.* For more specific information about interval and elite-level running, you can refer to *The Total Runner's Almanac.* The almanac, used by many world-class runners, contains detailed running programs for intermediate to elite runners, including charts to determine interval running and pacing, goal setting, race planning, and so on.

Exercise Physiology Definitions

Resting heart rate (RHR): Your heart rate at complete rest, that is, before rising in the morning. The RHR can be decreased with training.

Lactic acid: A metabolic waste product that accumulates in your system during exercise, causing fatigue. The heavier the exercise, the more lactic acid accumulates. The term is often used synonymously with *lactates,* which is close enough (a lactate is a buffered lactic acid). A lactic acid blood level, molarity or concentration, of 2 mM (millimoles per liter) is sometimes regarded as the aerobic threshold and 4 mM as the anaerobic threshold, though these values vary by individual.

Aerobic capacity level: The exercise intensity level at which your body's oxygen consumption is in balance with your metabolic waste products. Some researchers believe this is the minimum training level that will produce an endurance effect; they call it the *aerobic threshold.*

Anaerobic capacity level, or anaerobic threshold (AT): The intensity level after which any increase in speed will cause a linear increase in lactic acid. Experts do not agree on the exact point at which the AT is reached. Still, you can improve your AT, and thus your performance, with training. In the early season you may reach your AT at 140 BPM, mid-season at 150 BPM and late season at 160+ BPM, assuming you train properly. Some experts claim that the AT is a fixed value that cannot be changed.

Maximum oxygen consumption, or uptake (VO_2max): A scientific value defined as the maximum amount of oxygen per minute of exercise that you are able to consume. This maximum rate is reached at a slower than maximum speed. (Your *anaerobic capacity* makes it possible for you to continue beyond this level. Your body then supplies energy even though the oxygen availability is inadequate and metabolic waste products are produced.) The VO_2max can be increased with training.

Maximum heart rate (MHR): The heart rate right before exhaustion at a maximum work load. The MHR cannot be increased with training. It decreases with age.

Running Your Best Race

The three most common road race distances are the 5 km, the 10 km and the marathon.

THE PACING DILEMMA

The universal dilemma is that of pacing. If you are too conservative, you will reach the finish with energy to spare, knowing that had you been more courageous you would have been faster. Conversely, if you get caught up in the mass hysteria of the start and go out too fast—which is easy to do when you are rested—you will watch, physically depleted, while other runners pass you.

COMMON GUIDELINES

Below are some universal truths about racing.

1. Get plenty of rest. Eat moderate quantities of easily digestible foods (see "Nutrition" on page 11).

2. Arrive early at the race site. You need time to warm up, stretch and visit the portable toilets a few times.

3. At the starting line, position yourself on one side and by the marker for the pace you want to run (often the pace per mile or km is marked by signs).

4. Stay relaxed and keep things in perspective. Remember, it's neither your last race nor the last day of your life.

THE 10 KM RACE

Most experienced runners agree that the 10 km road race is the most difficult to run. It is too short to start out slowly, yet it is too long to go all out. Pacing is critical.

1. When the gun goes off, stay within yourself. If you have a goal time, know that pace and stick to it.

2. Expect to run the first mile a little faster than the pace you want to average, but not more than 20 seconds faster. If your speed feels a little slow, that is probably good.

3. Run the first half of the first mile slower than the second half. This tactic is called a negative split of that mile.

4. Look straight ahead with tunnel vision. Visualize yourself relaxed and feeling strong. Your arms and shoulders are loose; and you are running like the wind. As Joy Leutner says, "Run like an Indian, light with your feet."

If you have paced yourself properly very few people will pass you after the first ten minutes. You are going to feel tired toward the end of the race, but your pace will remain strong.

THE 5 KM RACE

Most of the same rules apply for the 5 km race, except you can go out harder. It will hurt a bit more than the 10 km, but the pain doesn't last as long. And finishing a 5 km race with style will give you an instant feeling of euphoria.

1. Pay particular attention to warming up. The best formula is to start running easily about 40 minutes before the start of the race.

2. As you warm up, scope out the last mile or so of the course, checking for tight turns or hills, by running the course in reverse.

3. Stop and stretch, especially the hamstrings and calves. Incorporate no more than ten 50 meter pick-ups to nearly full speed. Warm down, then rest about 10 minutes.

4. When the gun goes off, look straight ahead and draw all energy inward. Turn off external sounds and concentrate on a pace that is right on the edge. Get up on your toes.

5. Don't allow thoughts of how bad you feel to enter your mind. You should feel that "this is hard." So what, it is!

6. Relax your jaw. This single act will have amazing results. Your shoulders will drop, your arms will swing freer, your chest will open up and you'll get more oxygen.

7. When you reach the last mile, tell yourself, "I've run a mile before" and hang on!

THE MARATHON RACE
Running a marathon, 42.2 km (26.2 miles), takes a bit more strategy. You must pace yourself, or pay the price for a very long time. You will be on the road much longer and probably through varied weather and road conditions.

1. Early morning starts can be cool. Wear an old shirt that you can throw away after the race starts.

2. It is often a good idea to lather your feet with petroleum jelly before putting on your socks. Your feet can get wet simply from running through the aid stations. This could lead to painful blood blisters.

3. Unless you're wearing a very soft top, put band-aids or petroleum jelly on your nipples to prevent chaffing.

4. Start out painfully slowly and pay attention to your breathing. Run the first 20 miles at a conversational pace. The second half starts at 20 miles so try to reach that point with energy to spare. You will feel tired, but the last six miles can be very long if you have not prepared properly.

5. Drink. If you plan to use an electrolyte replacement, it is best to hold off until later in the race. Dilute it by also drinking water. You could also try one of the many energy bars or gels on the market—assuming, of course, you have used them in training first.

If all goes well, you will finish feeling elated. Several hours later, you will not be able to get up from a chair or walk downstairs. But hey, who cares!

Strength Training

Originally the domain of bodybuilders and weight lifters, the gym also attracts athletes seeking to develop sports-specific strength or to rehabilitate after an injury.

This chapter provides general guidelines for developing a general strength program at the gym by using the most commonly available equipment. It does not, however, outline specific exercises or workouts, which is considered the domain of a professional trainer.

Strength training is not only for building bulk. Research in physiology clearly shows that strength training is essential for optimum endurance and performance. It is also well documented that we lose muscle mass during prolonged nonresistance exercise, such as running. We also lose more muscle mass as we get older.

THINGS TO KNOW ABOUT THE GYM

A gym most often has two exercise areas, one for aerobics and one for strength training. The aerobics area has a variety of cardiovascular exercise machines such as bicycles, stair climbers and treadmills. Some machines work only your legs, while others work your upper body as well. The strength area is equipped with resistance machines and free weights; free weights are further divided into dumbbells and barbells.

CARDIOVASCULAR EQUIPMENT

In most gyms, the "cardio section" used to be tucked away in a corner. The area was small and contained a rowing machine, a few exercise bicycles and perhaps a treadmill. In the last few years, however, this section has been substantially expanded. Interest in cardiovascular workouts has increased, and the cardio rooms are significantly larger and better equipped.

Much new exercise equipment has also been brought to market. The innovation has primarily been manifest in combined upper and lower body machinery and more advanced electronic controls.

STRENGTH EQUIPMENT

Most people who go to the weight room for the first time are more comfortable using the resistance machines than the free weights. There are advantages and disadvantages to each. Machines are generally safer and require less skill to operate; they also provide a very specific and predetermined range of motion for one or several muscle groups. Some machines are designed to load the muscle more evenly throughout its entire range of motion for a better, or different, training effect.

Free weights are simpler. It's just you, the weight and gravity. But, unless you know what you're doing, free weights can be dangerous. Dropping a dumbbell or a plate on your toe, even a light one, is not a pleasant experience. However, free weights add important elements of balance and coordination to your exercise, among other things. Talk to your trainer or the gym staff about how best to use them.

CLOTHING

Most people go to the gym in clothing that allows plenty of free motion. Though some gyms have stricter regulations for proper apparel, *clean* running shoes and clothes are generally fine.

STRENGTH TRAINING GUIDELINES

The following is a list of strength training tips and common "gym customs." You will also find strength training templates in the appendix, starting on page 91.

1. Start out easily. Just because the woman half your size bench presses two big plates, it doesn't mean you can. The first week or so, be content with bench pressing the bar alone and use very tiny weights. Also, if you have been away from the gym for more than a week, start out with considerably less weight than when you left off.

2. Beware of the lure of the heavy weight. Lifting weights that are too heavy will cause you to strain, lose form and *decrease* the training effect. Even after you get used to weight training, increase your weights gradually over time.

3. Work your entire body. You need to develop a program that exercises all major muscle groups. Don't just focus on your arms and legs; remember that your trunk, or *core,* (abdominal, side, and upper and lower back muscles) is just as important for fitness. The core exercises provide critical stability to the skeleton where the muscles of the extremities attach.

4. Find an instructor and/or a partner. If you are unfamiliar with the equipment in the gym or you have limited knowledge about anatomy or strength training, it is best to seek out a trainer. Most gyms have certified strength instructors who can show you exactly which equipment to use, as well as how and why. After only a few sessions, you should be able to train on your own, or with a partner.

5. Find a spotter. When lifting heavy weights, such as with the bench press or squats, always have somebody watch you. The spotter is there to assist you, if necessary. If you don't have a partner, just courteously ask somebody to spot you for a minute. The person you ask will gladly help you and even provide needed encouragement to finish those last reps when the going gets tough.

6. Don't hold your breath. Some people follow a breathing pattern when lifting weights—such as exhaling on exertion—others don't. Just never hold your breath, as this will limit your oxygen supply and may cause you to faint—even if you're a big boy.

7. Wear a weight lifting belt. Protect and stabilize your lower back and torso by wearing a weight lifting belt during demanding exercises such as squats. The best belts are made of leather.

8. Follow the rules. Never leave plates on the bar or dumbbells on the floor when you are finished, even if that's where you found them. Always put the weights (bars, barbells, dumbbells and plates) back in their racks. Also, obey the rules of the club. Each club has a set of safety and courtesy guidelines that you must follow—remember, there's almost *always* somebody bigger than you at the gym!

9. Load and stack plates properly. Plates have one side with the weight stamped on it (the face), and one blank side. You load the bar with the plate face in; you stack the plate back on the rack face out.

10. Alternate exercises. If you go to the gym specifically to "build" muscle mass—say in the off-season—you need to alternate exercises. One day you focus on the upper body, the next on the lower body. During the season, strength training is only a complement to your other training, when going to the gym two to four times a week is sufficient.

Important: If you are interested in a detailed strength training program designed specifically for endurance athletes, try the video *Strength Training for Total Body Fitness,* featuring Ironman champions Mark Allen and Paula Newby-Fraser with certified fitness specialist Diane Buchta.

Helping out with this chapter was Ross Gerry, the assistant women's swim coach at Stanford University. Ross has a Master of Education degree from Boston University, with a specialty in human movement. He is a certified strength and conditioning specialist (CSCS) of the National Strength and Conditioning Association (NSCA). He also coaches the Stanford Masters swim team, which tests his vast knowledge, immeasurable patience and good sense of humor every day.

Heart Rate Monitor Training

The heart rate monitor, as we know it, was developed in Finland. With their great tradition of endurance sports, the Finns proceeded to establish simple and practical procedures for optimizing the use of their creation.

The heart rate monitor is an excellent tool for the serious runner. The monitor gives a continuous read-out of what's really happening to your system, your heart in particular, when you expose it to stress. And your heart never lies.

The object of this chapter is to combine some of the latest research—in itself open to interpretation—with the practical experience of the Finns, arguably the world's leading practitioners of endurance training with heart rate monitors. If you are not familiar with the basic principles of exercise physiology, there is a list of definitions on page 20.

CARDIOVASCULAR TRAINING OBJECTIVES

Many exercise physiologists believe that raising your AT is the most important factor in enhancing your performance in a distance race; others tend to focus on the aerobic threshold. Actually, improvement in your thresholds reflects a series of physiological changes in your body such as a VO_2max increase, a reduction in muscle lactate production and an improvement in lactate removal from your muscles. Continuous training also increases your heart's stroke volume, your blood volume and the number of red blood cells.

FIXED HEART RATE ZONES—A FALSE ASSUMPTION

For competitive or recreational runners, there are no universal fixed percentages of the MHR that will optimally improve performance. Yes, there *are* observable correlations between a person's MHR and what is happening physiologically in the body when one exercises—but they are not that obvious. First, the heart rate correlations are only approximations. Second, they are highly individual. And third, they are not static, but rather dynamic over time. To train with a goal of maintaining certain fixed percentages of your MHR, therefore, carries with it a high risk of undertraining, or worse (runners can be quite driven), overtraining.

TESTING WITH A HEART RATE MONITOR

In order to get maximum benefit from the heart rate monitor, you need to understand its basic operation (read the manual) and undergo a series of tests.

THE HEART RATE MONITOR

A heart rate monitor has three parts:

• A wrist monitor (looks like a digital watch)

• A sensor/transmitter (a flexible plastic stripe, often black)

• An elastic chest band

To use a monitor, attach the sensor/transmitter to your chest with the chest band, and strap the monitor to your wrist. If the monitor does not display your heart rate, put some saliva on the sensor/transmitter next to your skin to increase the conductivity. After you have reread the warning on page 6, you're ready to roll.

TESTING WITH ACCESS TO A LABORATORY

Finnish athletes undergo testing on a treadmill in a lab while their blood lactate levels are measured. Then tests are done on a track. Sometimes lab testing is not possible, in which case only the track is used. All training is based on the most recent results.

The Direct Test. The lab test on a treadmill is called a *direct test,* which means that the load is increased gradually (often every three minutes) until exhaustion. Blood lactate levels are continuously measured. Let's say you reach your aerobic capacity at a pace of 4 min/km with a heart rate of 145 BPM, and that your MHR is 185. Your aerobic capacity is thus 40 BPM below your MHR at a pace of 4 min/km. (Generally, the aerobic capacity is approximately 40 (+/-5) BPM and the anaerobic capacity approximately 20 (+/-10) BPM below the MHR. In a less fit person, these heart rates may vary more.)

The Track Test. In the track test you determine your aerobic capacity without measuring lactates. Let's say that with a heart rate of 145 BPM you now require 4:10 to run one kilometer. The difference is 10 seconds. This means that under real conditions you can expect your aerobic pace to be 10 seconds slower. If your pace is 10 seconds *faster* on the track, you are probably unaccustomed to running on a treadmill. As you get used to the treadmill, your track and treadmill results will converge.

TESTING WITHOUT ACCESS TO A LABORATORY

If you do not have access to a lab, you can do the following tests on a track.

The Max Test. Warm up for about 15 minutes. Then run 100 m fast two to three times. Then run 400 m by accelerating so that for the last 60 to 80 m you are going as fast as you can (you must exhaust yourself). Check your heart rate. Your aerobic and anaerobic capacities are approximately 40 and 20 BPM below your MHR, respectively.

The Aerobic Test. After warm-up, run one kilometer on the track at your aerobic capacity (say 145 BPM). Early in the season your time may be 4:10. Later in the season, you should be able to run the same distance faster with the same heart rate. You can also factor in your perceived level of effort to determine your aerobic level. Think of this intensity as "Fast, but I can keep going forever, or almost forever."

HEART RATE BASED TRAINING

Optimal training is based on a given work load; in our example, an aerobic threshold of 145 BPM. For the next few months, with this threshold, an LSD run—by definition, almost completely aerobic—would be between 120 and 130 BPM. An AT run would be in the 145 to 160 BPM range. During high-intensity intervals, the heart rate would go above 160 BPM.

Important: As you get fitter, and if you train properly, your thresholds will move upward. What may have been an anaerobic session early in the season will become a primarily aerobic session later on, and years later may be an endurance pace that you can keep up "indefinitely."

YOUR WEEKLY TRAINING SCHEDULE

You will notice that— just as there are no recipes in the nutrition chapter, nor specific exercises in the strength training chapter—this book contains no sample weekly workouts. There are two primary reasons for this omission: First, providing a weekly workout is a guessing game—even for an experienced coach working with a well-conditioned, competitive athlete. Second, there are just too many unknowns. If your schedule says "run 15 km at 150 BPM on Tuesday" and you cannot do this, then it is likely that you will have to modify the rest of that week's schedule, as well.

Instead, you need to develop a personal schedule that takes into account the components of the general overview of running levels shown in the chart on page 84. It lists the daily and weekly run ranges in both kilometers and miles. Combining these running ranges with your running objectives and the other variables in your life will help you flesh out a weekly and monthly schedule that can work for you. The only other sane alternative would be to get a coach.

This chapter benefited from the expertise of Seppo Nuuttila, a former coach of the Finnish National Track and Field Team and a long-time coach of several Olympic and professional endurance athletes, including duathletes, rowers, runners and triathletes.

Date/Day					Notes	Intensity
Mo						
Tu						
We						
Th						
Fr						
Sa						
Su						
Weekly Total						
Year to Date						

the total runner's log

Focus: _____   Week: _____

Date/Day					Notes	Intensity
Mo						
Tu						
We						
Th						
Fr						
Sa						
Su						
Weekly Total						
Year to Date						

the total runner's log

Focus: Week:

Date/Day					Notes	Intensity
Mo						
Tu						
We						
Th						
Fr						
Sa						
Su						
Weekly Total						
Year to Date						

the total runner's log

Focus: _____   Week: _____

the total runner's log

Date/Day						Notes	Intensity
Mo							
Tu							
We							
Th							
Fr							
Sa							
Su							
Weekly Total							
Year to Date							

Date/Day					Notes	Intensity
Mo						
Tu						
We						
Th						
Fr						
Sa						
Su						
Weekly Total						
Year to Date						

the total runner's log

Focus: _____   Week: _____

the total runner's log

Date/Day						Notes	Intensity
Mo							
Tu							
We							
Th							
Fr							
Sa							
Su							
Weekly Total							
Year to Date							

Date/Day						Notes	Intensity
Mo							
Tu							
We							
Th							
Fr							
Sa							
Su							
Weekly Total							
Year to Date							

the total runner's log

Focus: _____   Week: _____

Date/Day						Notes	Intensity
Mo							
Tu							
We							
Th							
Fr							
Sa							
Su							
Weekly Total							
Year to Date							

the total runner's log

cus: Week:

ate/Day					Notes	Intensity
Mo						
Tu						
We						
Th						
Fr						
Sa						
Su						
Weekly Total						
ear to Date						

the total runner's log

Focus:

the total runner's log

Date/Day						Notes	Intensity
Mo							
Tu							
We							
Th							
Fr							
Sa							
Su							
Weekly Total							
Year to Date							

Date/Day					Notes	Intensity
Mo						
Tu						
We						
Th						
Fr						
Sa						
Su						
Weekly Total						
Year to Date						

Focus: Week:

Date/Day					Notes	Intensity
Mo						
Tu						
We						
Th						
Fr						
Sa						
Su						
Weekly Total						
Year to Date						

the total runner's log

Date/Day					Notes	Intensity
Mo						
Tu						
We						
Th						
Fr						
Sa						
Su						
Weekly Total						
Year to Date						

the total runner's log

Focus: Week:

the total runner's log

Date/Day						Notes	Intensity
Mo							
Tu							
We							
Th							
Fr							
Sa							
Su							
Weekly Total							
Year to Date							

Date/Day					Notes	Intensity
Mo						
Tu						
We						
Th						
Fr						
Sa						
Su						
Weekly Total						
Year to Date						

Focus: Week:

Date/Day					Notes	Intensity
Mo						
Tu						
We						
Th						
Fr						
Sa						
Su						
Weekly Total						
Year to Date						

the total runner's log

Date/Day					Notes	Intensity
Mo						
Tu						
We						
Th						
Fr						
Sa						
Su						
Weekly Total						
Year to Date						

the total runner's log

the total runner's log

Date/Day					Notes	Intensity
Mo						
Tu						
We						
Th						
Fr						
Sa						
Su						
Weekly Total						
Year to Date						

Focus: Week:

Date/Day						Notes	Intensity
Mo							
Tu							
We							
Th							
Fr							
Sa							
Su							
Weekly Total							
Year to Date							

the total runner's log

Focus: _____   Week: _____

the total runner's log

Date/Day					Notes	Intensity
Mo						
Tu						
We						
Th						
Fr						
Sa						
Su						
Weekly Total						
Year to Date						

Focus: Week:

Date/Day						Notes	Intensity
Mo							
Tu							
We							
Th							
Fr							
Sa							
Su							
Weekly Total							
Year to Date							

the total runner's log

Focus: _____   Week: _____

Date/Day					Notes	Intensity
Mo						
Tu						
We						
Th						
Fr						
Sa						
Su						
Weekly Total						
Year to Date						

the total runner's log

Focus: _____   Week: _____

Date/Day					Notes	Intensity
Mo						
Tu						
We						
Th						
Fr						
Sa						
Su						
Weekly Total						
Year to Date						

the total runner's log

Focus: Week:

Date/Day					Notes	Intensity
Mo						
Tu						
We						
Th						
Fr						
Sa						
Su						
Weekly Total						
Year to Date						

the total runner's log

ocus: Week:

Date/Day					Notes	Intensity
Mo						
Tu						
We						
Th						
Fr						
Sa						
Su						
Weekly Total						
Year to Date						

the total runner's log

Focus: _____   Week: _____

Date/Day					Notes	Intensity
Mo						
Tu						
We						
Th						
Fr						
Sa						
Su						
Weekly Total						
Year to Date						

the total runner's log

ocus: Week:

Date/Day					Notes	Intensity
Mo						
Tu						
We						
Th						
Fr						
Sa						
Su						
Weekly Total						
Year to Date						

the total runner's log

Focus: _____   Week: _____

Date/Day					Notes	Intensity
Mo						
Tu						
We						
Th						
Fr						
Sa						
Su						
Weekly Total						
Year to Date						

the total runner's log

Focus: Week:

Date/Day						Notes	Intensity
Mo							
Tu							
We							
Th							
Fr							
Sa							
Su							
Weekly Total							
Year to Date							

Focus: Week:

Date/Day						Notes	Intensity
Mo							
Tu							
We							
Th							
Fr							
Sa							
Su							
Weekly Total							
Year to Date							

the total runner's log

cus: Week:

Date/Day						Notes	Intensity
Mo							
Tu							
We							
Th							
Fr							
Sa							
Su							
Weekly Total							
Year to Date							

the total runner's log

Focus:

the total runner's log

Date/Day					Notes	Intensity
Mo						
Tu						
We						
Th						
Fr						
Sa						
Su						
Weekly Total						
Year to Date						

Date/Day					Notes	Intensity
Mo						
Tu						
We						
Th						
Fr						
Sa						
Su						
Weekly Total						
Year to Date						

the total runner's log

Focus: _____   Week: _____

the total runner's log

Date/Day					Notes	Intensity
Mo						
Tu						
We						
Th						
Fr						
Sa						
Su						
Weekly Total						
Year to Date						

ate/Day						Notes	Intensity
Mo							
Tu							
We							
Th							
Fr							
Sa							
Su							
Weekly Total							
Year to Date							

the total runner's log

Focus: Week:

the total runner's log

Date/Day					Notes	Intensity
Mo						
Tu						
We						
Th						
Fr						
Sa						
Su						
Weekly Total						
Year to Date						

ocus: Week:

Date/Day						Notes	Intensity
Mo							
Tu							
We							
Th							
Fr							
Sa							
Su							
Weekly Total							
Year to Date							

the total runner's log

Focus: _____   Week: _____

Date/Day						Notes		Intensity
Mo								
Tu								
We								
Th								
Fr								
Sa								
Su								
Weekly Total								
Year to Date								

the total runner's log

cus: Week:

ate/Day					Notes	Intensity
Mo						
Tu						
We						
Th						
Fr						
Sa						
Su						
Weekly Total						
ear to Date						

the total runner's log

Focus:

the total runner's log

Date/Day					Notes	Intensity
Mo						
Tu						
We						
Th						
Fr						
Sa						
Su						
Weekly Total						
Year to Date						

Date/Day					Notes		Intensity
Mo							
Tu							
We							
Th							
Fr							
Sa							
Su							
Weekly Total							
Year to Date							

the total runner's log

Focus:

the total runner's log

Date/Day					Notes	Intensity
Mo						
Tu						
We						
Th						
Fr						
Sa						
Su						
Weekly Total						
Year to Date						

Focus: _____   Week: _____

Date/Day						Notes	Intensity
Mo							
Tu							
We							
Th							
Fr							
Sa							
Su							
Weekly Total							
Year to Date							

the total runner's log

Focus: _____   Week: _____

Date/Day						Notes	Intensity
Mo							
Tu							
We							
Th							
Fr							
Sa							
Su							
Weekly Total							
Year to Date							

the total runner's log

cus: Week:

ate/Day					Notes	Intensity
Mo						
Tu						
We						
Th						
Fr						
Sa						
Su						
Weekly Total						
ear to Date						

the total runner's log

Focus: Week:

the total runner's log

Date/Day						Notes	Intensity
Mo							
Tu							
We							
Th							
Fr							
Sa							
Su							
Weekly Total							
Year to Date							

ate/Day					Notes	Intensity
Mo						
Tu						
We						
Th						
Fr						
Sa						
Su						
Veekly Total						
ear to Date						

the total runner's log

Focus: _____   Week: _____

Date/Day						Notes	Intensity
Mo							
Tu							
We							
Th							
Fr							
Sa							
Su							
Weekly Total							
Year to Date							

the total runner's log

Focus: _____   Week: _____

Date/Day						Notes	Intensity
Mo							
Tu							
We							
Th							
Fr							
Sa							
Su							
Weekly Total							
Year to Date							

the total runner's log

Focus: Week:

Date/Day						Notes	Intensity
Mo							
Tu							
We							
Th							
Fr							
Sa							
Su							
Weekly Total							
Year to Date							

the total runner's log

Date/Day					Notes	Intensity
Mo						
Tu						
We						
Th						
Fr						
Sa						
Su						
Weekly Total						
Year to Date						

the total runner's log

Focus: _____   Week: _____

the total runner's log

Date/Day						Notes	Intensity
Mo							
Tu							
We							
Th							
Fr							
Sa							
Su							
Weekly Total							
Year to Date							

Focus: Week:

Date/Day					Notes	Intensity
Mo						
Tu						
We						
Th						
Fr						
Sa						
Su						
Weekly Total						
Year to Date						

the total runner's log

How to Use Your Weekly Overview

On the next page you will find examples of several ways to keep your weekly overview. Each day has a slightly different system, described below. In general, a simple system is easier to maintain and understand.

Training Focus and Week Numbering. In the upper left corner of the page is the word *focus* where you can indicate weekly training focus. In the upper right corner is the word *week* where you can indicate time of year.

1 Monday. This day at the gym consisted of a 30-minute run using the treadmill's program four, followed by one hour of strength training with free weights.

2 Tuesday. This person records how she feels, on a five-point scale where 1 is sick, 3 is good and 5 is great. Tuesday was a "good" day. She slept eight hours, had a morning resting heart rate of 52 bpm and a morning weight of 50 kg. She ran for one hour and got a chiropractic adjustment.

3 Wednesday. This person uses distances and an intensity scale of low, medium and high. In the morning, she ran 15 km at high intensity (85 to 100 percent of maximum heart rate) and in the evening 5 km at a low intensity (less than 70 percent). The other recordings are similar to those of Tuesday's person, but abbreviated. The day was "very good" (F: 4), the morning heart rate 50 bpm, the morning weight 53 kg, all after nine hours of sleep.

4 Thursday. This person ran 10 km in a time of 41:05, with a halfway split of 21:15 and then stretched and did abdominals for an hour. He uses a heart rate monitor to record maximum (158) and average (118) heart rates, as well as time in target zone (72 percent).

5 Friday. These entries are similar to Thursday's, but this runner records hours trained rather than distances, as well as an average intensity for the day.

6 Saturday. This is an ultrarunner: she has recorded a four-hour trail run with friends. In the afternoon she did static active stretching for one hour.

7 Sunday. This runner had the time of his life, finishing the tenth annual Your Worst Nightmare 10K in 1 hour and 20 minutes, a seven to nine mile annual event in southern California.

Focus: **WEEKLY OVERVIEW**   Week:

Day/Date	Run 1	Run 2		Stretch	Strength	Notes	Intensity
Mo							
Tu							
We							
Th							
Fr							
Sa							
Su							
Weekly Total							
Year to Date							

OVERVIEW OF RUNNING LEVELS—GENERAL

Parameter		Phase One Adaptation	Phase Two Structure	Phase Three Intervals
Objectives		Build confidence Learn skills	Differentiate training Increase intensity and volume	Further differentiation Improve skills Prepare for first race
Duration		4 weeks to 1 year	6 weeks to 6 months	6 weeks and on
Daily Run Range	Metric (km)	3 - 12	6 - 15	8 - 25
	USA (miles)	2 - 8	4 - 10	5 - 15
Runs per week		3	4	5 - 6+
Weekly Run Range	Metric (km)	10 - 25	30 - 45	45 - 90+
	USA (miles)	5 - 15	20 - 30	30 - 60+
Comments		Add one run per week near the end of phase one	Always take a day off after your long or your hard run	Decrease your weekly run distance by 10% for the first several weeks when starting intervals

OVERVIEW OF RUNNING LEVELS—PERSONAL

Objectives				
Duration				
Daily Run Range	Distance			
	Notes			
Runs per week				
Weekly Run Range	Distance			
	Notes			
Additional Comments				

Focus:

INTERVAL TRAINING

Type/Set	Number of Repeats	Distance	Time	Interval or Recovery	Notes

INTERVAL TRAINING

Type/Set	Number of Repeats	Distance	Time	Interval or Recovery	Notes

INTERVAL TRAINING

Type/Set	Number of Repeats	Distance	Time	Interval or Recovery	Notes

Focus:

INTERVAL TRAINING

Type/Set	Number of Repeats	Distance	Time	Interval or Recovery	Notes

Focus:

STRENGTH TRAINING

Exercise	Set/Rep	Weight	Notes

Focus:

STRENGTH TRAINING

Exercise	Set/Rep	Weight	Notes

STRENGTH TRAINING

Exercise	Set/Rep	Weight	Notes

Focus:

STRENGTH TRAINING

Exercise	Set/Rep	Weight	Notes

PACE CHART—METRIC SYSTEM

Target Time				Split Times for the Following Distances							
5 km	10 km	1/2 Mar	Marathon	1 km	2 km	3 km	4 km	6 km	7 km	8 km	9 km
00:12:00	00:24:00	00:50:38	01:41:16	00:02:23	00:04:47	00:07:11	00:09:35	00:14:23	00:16:48	00:19:11	00:21:35
00:12:30	00:25:00	00:52:44	01:45:29	00:02:30	00:05:00	00:07:30	00:10:00	00:15:00	00:17:30	00:20:00	00:22:30
00:13:00	00:26:00	00:54:51	01:49:42	00:02:36	00:05:12	00:07:48	00:10:24	00:15:36	00:18:11	00:20:48	00:23:24
00:13:30	00:27:00	00:56:57	01:53:55	00:02:42	00:05:24	00:08:06	00:10:48	00:16:12	00:18:54	00:21:36	00:24:18
00:14:00	00:28:00	00:59:04	01:58:08	00:02:47	00:05:35	00:08:23	00:11:11	00:16:47	00:19:35	00:22:23	00:25:11
00:14:30	00:29:00	01:01:10	02:02:21	00:02:53	00:05:47	00:08:41	00:11:35	00:17:23	00:20:18	00:23:11	00:26:05
00:15:00	00:30:00	01:03:17	02:06:35	00:03:00	00:06:00	00:09:00	00:12:00	00:18:00	00:21:00	00:24:00	00:27:00
00:15:30	00:31:00	01:05:24	02:10:48	00:03:06	00:06:12	00:09:18	00:12:24	00:18:36	00:21:41	00:24:48	00:27:54
00:16:00	00:32:00	01:07:30	02:15:01	00:03:12	00:06:24	00:09:36	00:12:48	00:19:12	00:22:24	00:25:36	00:28:48
00:16:30	00:33:00	01:09:37	02:19:14	00:03:17	00:06:35	00:09:53	00:13:11	00:19:47	00:23:05	00:26:23	00:29:41
00:17:00	00:34:00	01:11:43	02:23:27	00:03:23	00:06:47	00:10:11	00:13:35	00:20:23	00:23:48	00:27:11	00:30:35
00:17:30	00:35:00	01:13:50	02:27:40	00:03:30	00:07:00	00:10:30	00:14:00	00:21:00	00:24:30	00:28:00	00:31:30
00:18:00	00:36:00	01:15:57	02:31:54	00:03:36	00:07:12	00:10:48	00:14:24	00:21:36	00:25:11	00:28:48	00:32:23
00:18:30	00:37:00	01:18:03	02:36:07	00:03:42	00:07:24	00:11:06	00:14:48	00:22:12	00:25:54	00:29:36	00:33:18
00:19:00	00:38:00	01:20:10	02:40:20	00:03:47	00:07:35	00:11:23	00:15:11	00:22:47	00:26:35	00:30:23	00:34:11
00:19:30	00:39:00	01:22:16	02:44:33	00:03:53	00:07:47	00:11:41	00:15:35	00:23:23	00:27:18	00:31:11	00:35:06
00:20:00	00:40:00	01:24:23	02:48:46	00:04:00	00:08:00	00:12:00	00:16:00	00:24:00	00:28:00	00:32:00	00:36:00
00:21:00	00:42:00	01:28:36	02:57:13	00:04:12	00:08:24	00:12:36	00:16:48	00:25:12	00:29:24	00:33:36	00:37:48
00:22:00	00:44:00	01:32:49	03:05:39	00:04:24	00:08:48	00:13:12	00:17:36	00:26:24	00:30:48	00:35:12	00:39:36
00:23:00	00:46:00	01:37:02	03:14:05	00:04:35	00:09:11	00:13:47	00:18:23	00:27:35	00:32:11	00:36:47	00:41:23
00:24:00	00:48:00	01:41:16	03:22:32	00:04:47	00:09:35	00:14:23	00:19:11	00:28:47	00:33:36	00:38:23	00:43:11
00:25:00	00:50:00	01:45:29	03:30:58	00:05:00	00:10:00	00:15:00	00:20:00	00:30:00	00:35:00	00:40:00	00:45:00
00:26:00	00:52:00	01:49:42	03:39:24	00:05:12	00:10:24	00:15:36	00:20:48	00:31:12	00:36:23	00:41:36	00:46:48
00:27:00	00:54:00	01:53:55	03:47:51	00:05:24	00:10:48	00:16:12	00:21:36	00:32:24	00:37:48	00:43:12	00:48:36
00:28:00	00:56:00	01:58:08	03:56:17	00:05:35	00:11:11	00:16:47	00:22:23	00:33:35	00:39:11	00:44:47	00:50:23
00:29:00	00:58:00	02:02:21	04:04:43	00:05:47	00:11:35	00:17:23	00:23:11	00:34:47	00:40:36	00:46:23	00:52:11
00:30:00	01:00:00	02:06:35	04:13:10	00:06:00	00:12:00	00:18:00	00:24:00	00:36:00	00:42:00	00:48:00	00:54:00

the total runner's log

PACE CHART—METRIC SYSTEM

Target Time				Split Times for the Following Distances							
5 km	10 km	1/2 Mar	Marathon	11 km	12 km	15 km	20 km	25 km	30 km	40 km	50 km
00:12:00	00:24:00	00:50:38	01:41:16	00:26:23	00:28:47	00:36:00	00:48:00	01:00:00	01:12:00	01:36:00	02:00:00
00:12:30	00:25:00	00:52:44	01:45:29	00:27:30	00:30:00	00:37:30	00:50:00	01:02:30	01:15:00	01:40:00	02:05:00
00:13:00	00:26:00	00:54:51	01:49:42	00:28:36	00:31:12	00:39:00	00:52:00	01:05:00	01:18:00	01:44:00	02:10:00
00:13:30	00:27:00	00:56:57	01:53:55	00:29:42	00:32:24	00:40:30	00:54:00	01:07:30	01:21:00	01:48:00	02:15:00
00:14:00	00:28:00	00:59:04	01:58:08	00:30:47	00:33:35	00:42:00	00:56:00	01:10:00	01:24:00	01:52:00	02:20:00
00:14:30	00:29:00	01:01:10	02:02:21	00:31:53	00:34:47	00:43:30	00:58:00	01:12:30	01:27:00	01:56:00	02:25:00
00:15:00	00:30:00	01:03:17	02:06:35	00:33:00	00:36:00	00:45:00	01:00:00	01:15:00	01:30:00	02:00:00	02:30:00
00:15:30	00:31:00	01:05:24	02:10:48	00:34:06	00:37:12	00:46:30	01:02:00	01:17:30	01:33:00	02:04:00	02:35:00
00:16:00	00:32:00	01:07:30	02:15:01	00:35:12	00:38:24	00:48:00	01:04:00	01:20:00	01:36:00	02:08:00	02:40:00
00:16:30	00:33:00	01:09:37	02:19:14	00:36:17	00:39:35	00:49:30	01:06:00	01:22:30	01:39:00	02:12:00	02:45:00
00:17:00	00:34:00	01:11:43	02:23:27	00:37:23	00:40:47	00:51:00	01:08:00	01:25:00	01:42:00	02:16:00	02:50:00
00:17:30	00:35:00	01:13:50	02:27:40	00:38:30	00:42:00	00:52:30	01:10:00	01:27:30	01:45:00	02:20:00	02:55:00
00:18:00	00:36:00	01:15:57	02:31:54	00:39:36	00:43:12	00:54:00	01:12:00	01:30:00	01:48:00	02:24:00	03:00:00
00:18:30	00:37:00	01:18:03	02:36:07	00:40:42	00:44:24	00:55:30	01:14:00	01:32:30	01:51:00	02:28:00	03:05:00
00:19:00	00:38:00	01:20:10	02:40:20	00:41:47	00:45:35	00:57:00	01:16:00	01:35:00	01:54:00	02:32:00	03:10:00
00:19:30	00:39:00	01:22:16	02:44:33	00:42:53	00:46:47	00:58:30	01:18:00	01:37:30	01:57:00	02:36:00	03:15:00
00:20:00	00:40:00	01:24:23	02:48:46	00:44:00	00:48:00	01:00:00	01:20:00	01:40:00	02:00:00	02:40:00	03:20:00
00:21:00	00:42:00	01:28:36	02:57:13	00:46:12	00:50:24	01:03:00	01:24:00	01:45:00	02:06:00	02:48:00	03:30:00
00:22:00	00:44:00	01:32:49	03:05:39	00:48:24	00:52:48	01:06:00	01:28:00	01:50:00	02:12:00	02:56:00	03:40:00
00:23:00	00:46:00	01:37:02	03:14:05	00:50:35	00:55:11	01:09:00	01:32:00	01:54:59	02:18:00	03:04:00	03:49:59
00:24:00	00:48:00	01:41:16	03:22:32	00:52:47	00:57:35	01:12:00	01:36:00	02:00:00	02:24:00	03:12:00	04:00:00
00:25:00	00:50:00	01:45:29	03:30:58	00:55:00	01:00:00	01:15:00	01:40:00	02:05:00	02:30:00	03:20:00	04:10:00
00:26:00	00:52:00	01:49:42	03:39:24	00:57:12	01:02:24	01:18:00	01:44:00	02:10:00	02:36:00	03:28:00	04:20:00
00:27:00	00:54:00	01:53:55	03:47:51	00:59:24	01:04:48	01:21:00	01:48:00	02:15:00	02:42:00	03:36:00	04:30:00
00:28:00	00:56:00	01:58:08	03:56:17	01:01:35	01:07:11	01:24:00	01:52:00	02:20:00	02:48:00	03:44:00	04:40:00
00:29:00	00:58:00	02:02:21	04:04:43	01:03:47	01:09:35	01:27:00	01:56:00	02:25:00	02:54:00	03:52:00	04:50:00
00:30:00	01:00:00	02:06:35	04:13:10	01:06:00	01:12:00	01:30:00	02:00:00	02:30:00	03:00:00	04:00:00	05:00:00

PACE CHART—US SYSTEM

Target Time				Split Times for the Following Distances							
5 km	10 km	1/2 Mar	Marathon	1 mi	2 mi	3 mi	4 mi	5 mi	6 mi	7 mi	8 mi
00:12:00	00:24:00	00:50:38	01:41:16	00:03:51	00:07:43	00:11:35	00:15:26	00:19:18	00:23:10	00:27:02	00:30:53
00:12:30	00:25:00	00:52:44	01:45:29	00:04:01	00:08:02	00:12:04	00:16:05	00:20:07	00:24:08	00:28:09	00:32:11
00:13:00	00:26:00	00:54:51	01:49:42	00:04:11	00:08:22	00:12:33	00:16:44	00:20:55	00:25:06	00:29:17	00:33:28
00:13:30	00:27:00	00:56:57	01:53:55	00:04:20	00:08:41	00:13:02	00:17:22	00:21:43	00:26:04	00:30:24	00:34:45
00:14:00	00:28:00	00:59:04	01:58:08	00:04:30	00:09:00	00:13:31	00:18:01	00:22:31	00:27:02	00:31:32	00:36:02
00:14:30	00:29:00	01:01:10	02:02:21	00:04:40	00:09:20	00:14:00	00:18:40	00:23:20	00:28:00	00:32:40	00:37:20
00:15:00	00:30:00	01:03:17	02:06:35	00:04:49	00:09:39	00:14:29	00:19:18	00:24:08	00:28:58	00:33:47	00:38:37
00:15:30	00:31:00	01:05:24	02:10:48	00:04:59	00:09:58	00:14:58	00:19:57	00:24:56	00:29:56	00:34:55	00:39:54
00:16:00	00:32:00	01:07:30	02:15:01	00:05:08	00:10:17	00:15:26	00:20:35	00:25:44	00:30:53	00:36:02	00:41:11
00:16:30	00:33:00	01:09:37	02:19:14	00:05:18	00:10:37	00:15:55	00:21:14	00:26:33	00:31:51	00:37:10	00:42:29
00:17:00	00:34:00	01:11:43	02:23:27	00:05:28	00:10:56	00:16:24	00:21:53	00:27:21	00:32:49	00:38:18	00:43:46
00:17:30	00:35:00	01:13:50	02:27:40	00:05:37	00:11:15	00:16:53	00:22:31	00:28:09	00:33:47	00:39:25	00:45:03
00:18:00	00:36:00	01:15:57	02:31:54	00:05:47	00:11:35	00:17:22	00:23:10	00:28:58	00:34:45	00:40:33	00:46:20
00:18:30	00:37:00	01:18:03	02:36:07	00:05:57	00:11:54	00:17:51	00:23:49	00:29:46	00:35:43	00:41:40	00:47:38
00:19:00	00:38:00	01:20:10	02:40:20	00:06:06	00:12:13	00:18:20	00:24:27	00:30:34	00:36:41	00:42:48	00:48:55
00:19:30	00:39:00	01:22:16	02:44:33	00:06:16	00:12:33	00:18:49	00:25:06	00:31:22	00:37:39	00:43:56	00:50:12
00:20:00	00:40:00	01:24:23	02:48:46	00:06:26	00:12:52	00:19:18	00:25:44	00:32:11	00:38:37	00:45:03	00:51:29
00:21:00	00:42:00	01:28:36	02:57:13	00:06:45	00:13:31	00:20:16	00:27:02	00:33:47	00:40:33	00:47:18	00:54:04
00:22:00	00:44:00	01:32:49	03:05:39	00:07:04	00:14:09	00:21:14	00:28:19	00:35:24	00:42:29	00:49:34	00:56:38
00:23:00	00:46:00	01:37:02	03:14:05	00:07:24	00:14:48	00:22:12	00:29:36	00:37:00	00:44:25	00:51:49	00:59:13
00:24:00	00:48:00	01:41:16	03:22:32	00:07:43	00:15:26	00:23:10	00:30:53	00:38:37	00:46:20	00:54:04	01:01:47
00:25:00	00:50:00	01:45:29	03:30:58	00:08:02	00:16:05	00:24:08	00:32:11	00:40:14	00:48:16	00:56:19	01:04:22
00:26:00	00:52:00	01:49:42	03:39:24	00:08:22	00:16:44	00:25:06	00:33:28	00:41:50	00:50:12	00:58:34	01:06:56
00:27:00	00:54:00	01:53:55	03:47:51	00:08:41	00:17:22	00:26:04	00:34:45	00:43:27	00:52:08	01:00:49	01:09:31
00:28:00	00:56:00	01:58:08	03:56:17	00:09:00	00:18:01	00:27:02	00:36:02	00:45:03	00:54:04	01:03:05	01:12:05
00:29:00	00:58:00	02:02:21	04:04:43	00:09:20	00:18:40	00:28:00	00:37:20	00:46:40	00:56:00	01:05:20	01:14:40
00:30:00	01:00:00	02:06:35	04:13:10	00:09:39	00:19:18	00:28:58	00:38:37	00:48:16	00:57:56	01:07:35	01:17:14

the total runner's log

PACE CHART—US SYSTEM

Target Time				Split Times for the Following Distances							
5 km	10 km	1/2 Mar	Marathon	10 mi	12 mi	14 mi	16 mi	18 mi	20 mi	22 mi	24 mi
00:12:00	00:24:00	00:50:38	01:41:16	00:38:37	00:46:20	00:54:04	01:01:47	01:09:31	01:17:14	01:24:58	01:32:41
00:12:30	00:25:00	00:52:44	01:45:29	00:40:14	00:48:16	00:56:19	01:04:22	01:12:25	01:20:28	01:28:30	01:36:33
00:13:00	00:26:00	00:54:51	01:49:42	00:41:50	00:50:12	00:58:34	01:06:56	01:15:19	01:23:41	01:32:03	01:40:25
00:13:30	00:27:00	00:56:57	01:53:55	00:43:27	00:52:08	01:00:49	01:09:31	01:18:12	01:26:54	01:35:35	01:44:17
00:14:00	00:28:00	00:59:04	01:58:08	00:45:03	00:54:04	01:03:05	01:12:05	01:21:06	01:30:07	01:39:08	01:48:08
00:14:30	00:29:00	01:01:10	02:02:21	00:46:40	00:56:00	01:05:20	01:14:40	01:24:00	01:33:20	01:42:40	01:52:00
00:15:00	00:30:00	01:03:17	02:06:35	00:48:16	00:57:56	01:07:35	01:17:14	01:26:54	01:36:33	01:46:13	01:55:52
00:15:30	00:31:00	01:05:24	02:10:48	00:49:53	00:59:52	01:09:50	01:19:49	01:29:48	01:39:46	01:49:45	01:59:44
00:16:00	00:32:00	01:07:30	02:15:01	00:51:29	01:01:47	01:12:05	01:22:23	01:32:41	01:42:59	01:53:17	02:03:35
00:16:30	00:33:00	01:09:37	02:19:14	00:53:06	01:03:43	01:14:21	01:24:58	01:35:35	01:46:13	01:56:50	02:07:27
00:17:00	00:34:00	01:11:43	02:23:27	00:54:43	01:05:39	01:16:36	01:27:32	01:38:29	01:49:26	02:00:22	02:11:19
00:17:30	00:35:00	01:13:50	02:27:40	00:56:19	01:07:35	01:18:51	01:30:07	01:41:23	01:52:39	02:03:55	02:15:11
00:18:00	00:36:00	01:15:57	02:31:54	00:57:56	01:09:31	01:21:06	01:32:41	01:44:17	01:55:52	02:07:27	02:19:02
00:18:30	00:37:00	01:18:03	02:36:07	00:59:32	01:11:27	01:23:21	01:35:16	01:47:10	01:59:05	02:11:00	02:22:54
00:19:00	00:38:00	01:20:10	02:40:20	01:01:09	01:13:23	01:25:37	01:37:50	01:50:04	02:02:18	02:14:32	02:26:46
00:19:30	00:39:00	01:22:16	02:44:33	01:02:45	01:15:19	01:27:52	01:40:25	01:52:58	02:05:31	02:18:04	02:30:38
00:20:00	00:40:00	01:24:23	02:48:46	01:04:22	01:17:14	01:30:07	01:42:59	01:55:52	02:08:44	02:21:37	02:34:29
00:21:00	00:42:00	01:28:36	02:57:13	01:07:35	01:21:06	01:34:37	01:48:08	02:01:39	02:15:11	02:28:42	02:42:13
00:22:00	00:44:00	01:32:49	03:05:39	01:10:48	01:24:58	01:39:08	01:53:17	02:07:27	02:21:37	02:35:47	02:49:56
00:23:00	00:46:00	01:37:02	03:14:05	01:14:01	01:28:50	01:43:38	01:58:26	02:13:15	02:28:03	02:42:51	02:57:40
00:24:00	00:48:00	01:41:16	03:22:32	01:17:14	01:32:41	01:48:08	02:03:35	02:19:02	02:34:29	02:49:56	03:05:23
00:25:00	00:50:00	01:45:29	03:30:58	01:20:28	01:36:33	01:52:39	02:08:44	02:24:50	02:40:56	02:57:01	03:13:07
00:26:00	00:52:00	01:49:42	03:39:24	01:23:41	01:40:25	01:57:09	02:13:53	02:30:38	02:47:22	03:04:06	03:20:50
00:27:00	00:54:00	01:53:55	03:47:51	01:26:54	01:44:17	02:01:39	02:19:02	02:36:25	02:53:48	03:11:11	03:28:34
00:28:00	00:56:00	01:58:08	03:56:17	01:30:07	01:48:08	02:06:10	02:24:11	02:42:13	03:00:14	03:18:16	03:36:17
00:29:00	00:58:00	02:02:21	04:04:43	01:33:20	01:52:00	02:10:40	02:29:20	02:48:00	03:06:41	03:25:21	03:44:01
00:30:00	01:00:00	02:06:35	04:13:10	01:36:33	01:55:52	02:15:11	02:34:29	02:53:48	03:13:07	03:32:26	03:51:44

ANNUAL SUMMARY

Week	Run				Notes

Week	Run				Notes
Total					

ANNUAL GRAPH

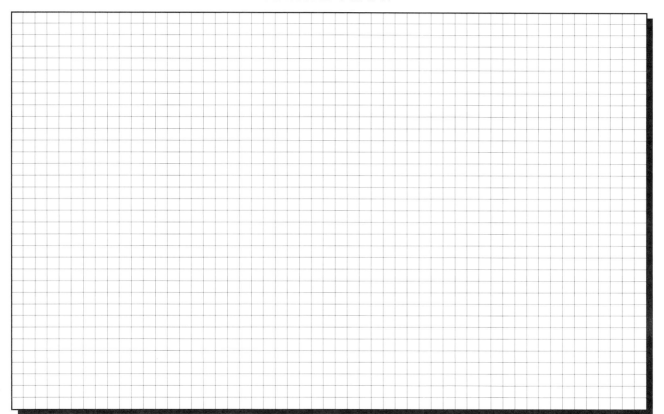

Note: Use this chart to plot your training values. Type of activity and intensity can be distinguished by using different colors and patterns in a bar chart, for instance. You may gain even more insight by correlating these graphic indicators with your weight, race results, feeling of well-being, and so on.

RACE RECORD

Date	Event	Distance	Time	Pace	Place	Notes

the total runner's log

ORDER FORM

TRIMARKET
THE COMPANY

The Trimarket Company
2264 Bowdoin Street
Palo Alto, CA 94306
USA

Phone: 1-650-494-1406
Fax: 1-650-494-1413

Web site: www.trimarket.com

Some titles are also available
at Amazon.com and other
leading book, fitness, sports
stores and web sites

International orders please submit an international money order drawn on a US bank

Please send me the following:

_____ each of **the total runner's log** *(third edition)* at $8.95   _____

_____ each of **the total runner's almanac - 3** *(third edition)* at $14.95   _____

_____ each of **the total fitness log** at $9.95   _____

_____ each of **finding the wheel's hub** by Scott Tinley at $9.95   _____

_____ each of **Can You Make a Living Doing That?** by Brad Kearns at $9.95   _____

_____ each of **the total triathlon almanac - 5** *(fifth edition)* at $18.95   _____

_____ each of **the total triathlon almanac - 4** *(fourth edition)* at $17.95   _____

_____ each of **the total triathlon almanac - 3** *(third edition)* at $16.95   _____

_____ each of **the total triathlon almanac - 1993** *(first edition)* at $16.95   _____

In California, add 8.25% sales tax   _____

Shipping, within USA $3.00 ($1.00 each additional)   _____

Shipping, priority (or international) $5.00 ($2.00 each additional)   _____

TOTAL

Name: _____

Address:_____

I understand that I may return any unused book for a full refund if not satisfied

OTHER POPULAR TRIMARKET TITLES

the total triathlon almanac-4

is the most detailed and comprehensive of all combined training logs and training handbooks. Specifically for the multisport athlete, this almanac is described by six-time Hawaii Ironman winner Mark Allen as, quote: "the best training manual and logbook on the market (and) Highly recommended."

the total runner's almanac-3

is a comprehensive logbook and training manual for the runner. Described by *Runner's World* magazine as, quote: "the Rolls Royce of training diaries (and) if you can only afford one running book this year, make it this one – it's worth it." Now with twice the room to write.

Can You Make a Living Doing That?
by Brad Kearns

Mark Allen describes this book as, quote: "a refreshing departure from the common 'how to' books in sports. Brad goes beyond the race results and workout miles to provide an intimate look at the lifestyle of a professional athlete. I highly recommend this book from one of the most colorful personalities in sports today."

finding the wheel's hub
by Scott Tinley

One of triathlon's enduring legends, this Ironman Hall of Famer tells it all in this his third book. Described by running's Bill Rodgers as, quote: "Scott Tinley brings you into the intense eye of the triathlon, spelling it out clearly and with a potent sense of humor. I found this a fascinating book."

Order form on reverse page